The Thinking Tree

MW00635579

BIRD Watching Journal

Nature Study & Backyard Science

Get to know all the Birds
in Your Neighborhood

Artwork & Design By:
Sarah Janisse Brown

North American Bird Drawings By:
Anna Kidalova

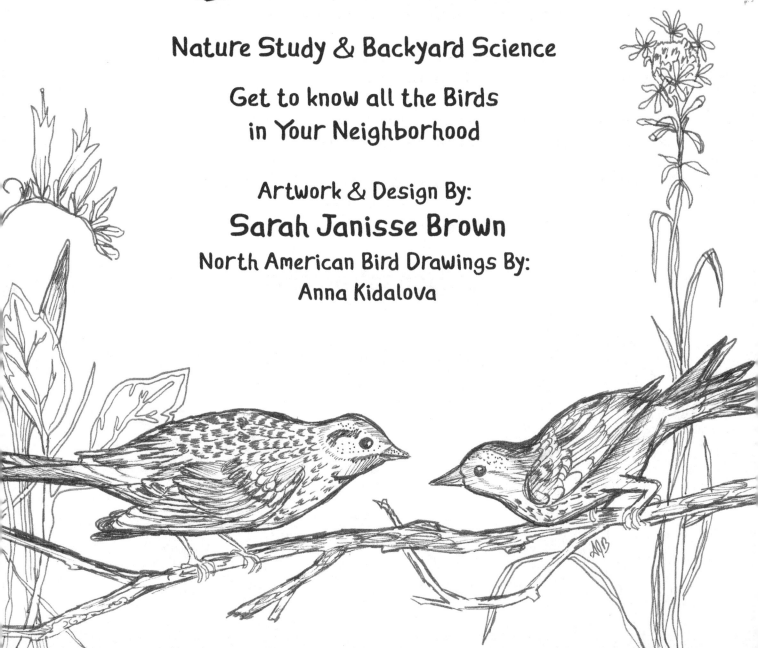

Introduction:

This is a research journal for bird watchers of all ages.
Bring this book with you on your adventures into the forest or into your backyard.
You will need a few tools to help you complete the activities in this journal, including
a bird identification handbook or field guide for your region, colored pencils,
binoculars, a camera, and some videos or documentaries about local birds.

You will research, observe and study the birds that you happen to see while you are
out bird watching. Find out the name of each bird in your area and learn everything
you can about it! What do they eat? What do their eggs look like? What sounds do
they make make? Do they migrate? What kind of nest do they build? What is the
difference between the male and female of each breed?

This book is perfect for creative students who love to draw, but if you don't enjoy
drawing just print photos and add them into this journal.

This book is perfect for anyone with a love for birds, but also can be used as a
science curriculum for homeschooling any grade level.

FunSchooling.com

Visit our website for more
Fun-Schooling Books!

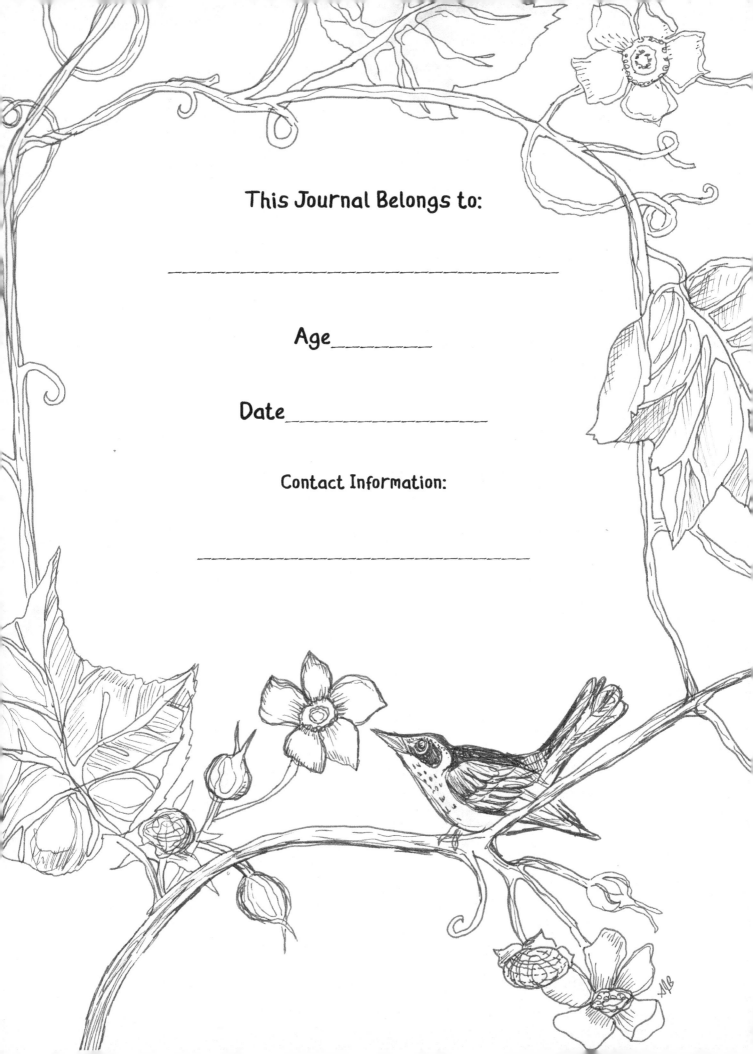

This Journal Belongs to:

_____

Age_____

Date_____

Contact Information:

_____

Type of Bird:

1st Day Spotted:

My Nest

My Egg

My Feathers

Draw Me

Research

Notes

My Habitat

My Food

My Enemies

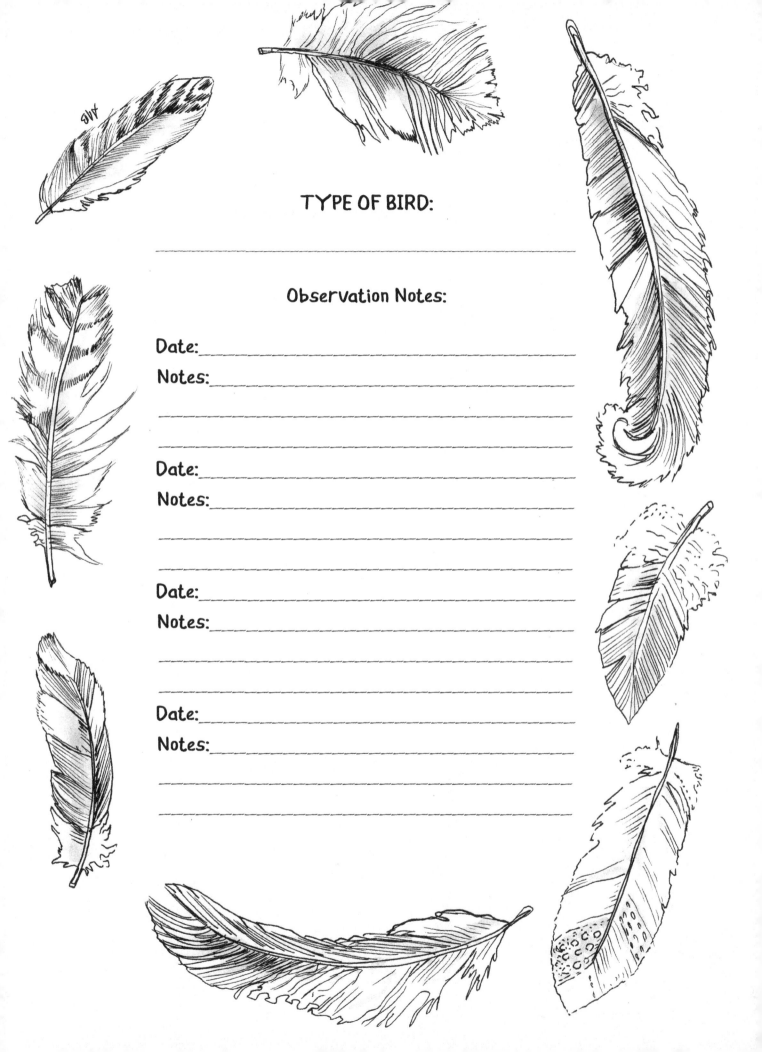

TYPE OF BIRD:

_____

Observation Notes:

Date:_____

Notes:_____

_____

_____

Date:_____

Notes:_____

_____

_____

Date:_____

Notes:_____

_____

_____

Date:_____

Notes:_____

_____

_____

TYPE OF BIRD:

Common Name: _____

Scientific Name: _____

Five Facts About This Type of Bird:

1._____
_____
_____

2._____
_____
_____

3._____
_____
_____

4._____
_____
_____

5._____
_____
_____
_____

Draw or Photograph a Female:

Draw or Photograph a Male:

Nature Poem:
(Copy one or write your own)

_____

_____

_____

_____

_____

_____

_____

_____

_____

_____

_____

Draw the Eggs of Different Types of Birds in Your Region

Research Challenge!

Can You Identify and Color Each North American Bird?

1._____

_____

2._____

_____

3._____

_____

4._____

_____

Take Photos and Tape One Here:

Watch a Documentary and Draw Your Favorite Parts:

Download and Print Beautiful Bird Photos:

Type of Bird:

1st Day Spotted:

My Nest

My Egg

Draw Me

My Feathers

Research

Notes

My Habitat

My Food

My Enemies

TYPE OF BIRD:
_____

Observation Notes:

Date:_____

Notes:_____

_____

_____

Date:_____

Notes:_____

_____

_____

Date:_____

Notes:_____

_____

_____

Date:_____

Notes:_____

_____

_____

TYPE OF BIRD:

Common Name: _____

Scientific Name: _____

Five Facts About This Type of Bird:

1. _____
_____
2. _____
_____
3. _____
_____
4. _____
_____
5. _____
_____
_____
_____
_____

Draw or Photograph a Female:

Draw or Photograph a Male:

Just for Fun

Write, Doodle or Sketch!

1976 USA

Research Challenge!

Can You Identify and Color Each North American Bird?

1._____

_____

_____

2._____

_____

_____

3._____

_____

_____

4._____

_____

Add Birds to the Drawing

What Kinds of Foods do the Birds in Your Neighborhood Eat?
Draw Examples:

Type of Bird:

1st Day Spotted:

My Nest

My Egg

My Feathers

Draw Me

Research

Notes

My Habitat

My Food

My Enemies

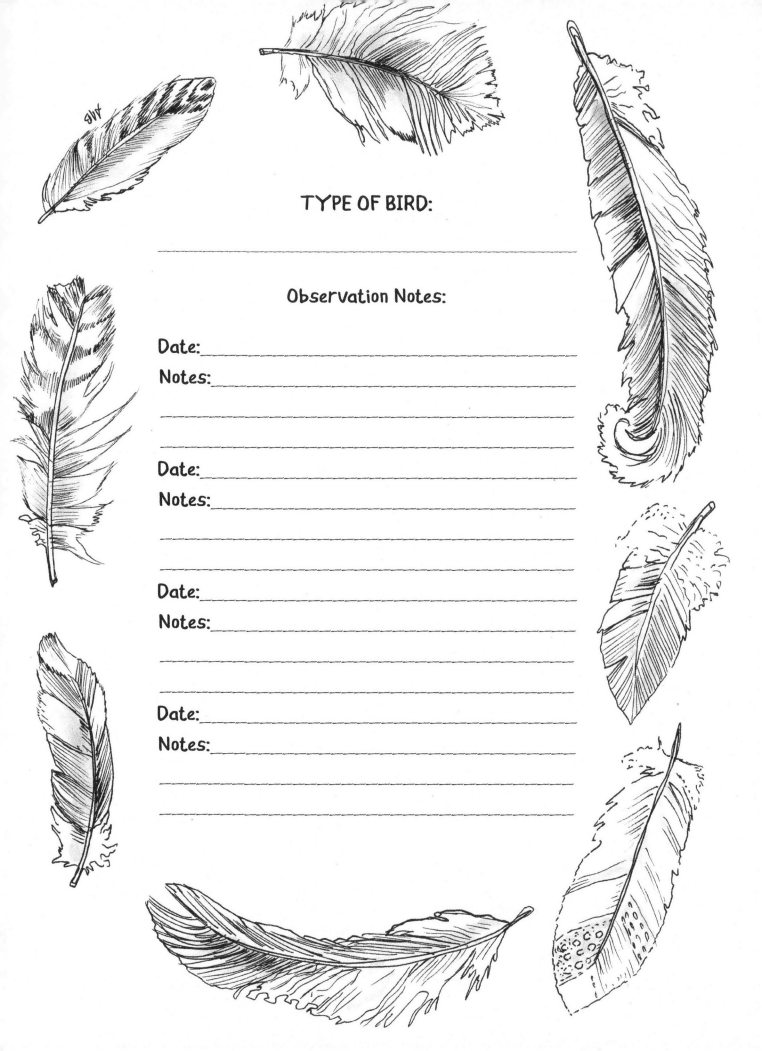

TYPE OF BIRD:

_____

Observation Notes:

Date:_____

Notes:_____

_____

_____

Date:_____

Notes:_____

_____

_____

Date:_____

Notes:_____

_____

_____

Date:_____

Notes:_____

_____

_____

TYPE OF BIRD:

Common Name: _____

Scientific Name: _____

Five Facts About This Type of Bird:

1._____

_____

_____

2._____

_____

3._____

_____

4._____

_____

5._____

_____

_____

_____

Draw or Photograph a Female:

Draw or Photograph a Male:

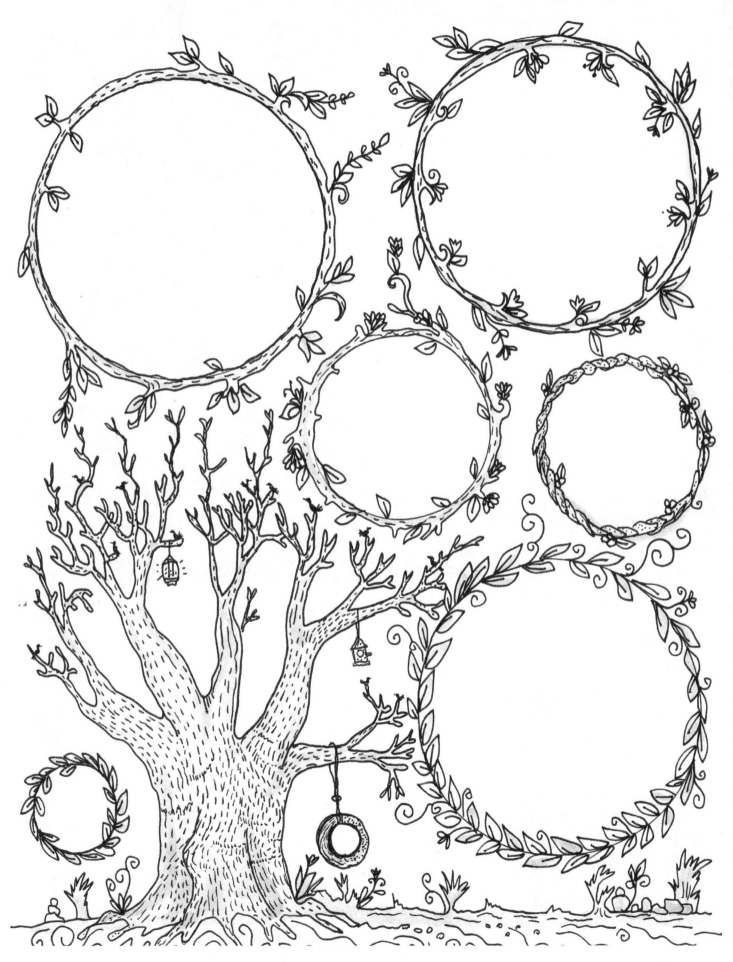

Read a Book about Birds and Take Notes:

_____

_____

_____

_____

_____

_____

_____

_____

_____

_____

Copy a picture from your book:

Nature Poem:
(Copy one or write your own)

_____

_____
_____
_____
_____
_____
_____
_____
_____
_____
_____
_____
_____
_____
_____

Type of Bird:

1st Day Spotted:

My Nest

My Egg

My Feathers

Draw Me

Research

Notes _____
_____
_____
_____
_____
_____
_____
_____
_____

My Habitat

My Food

My Enemies

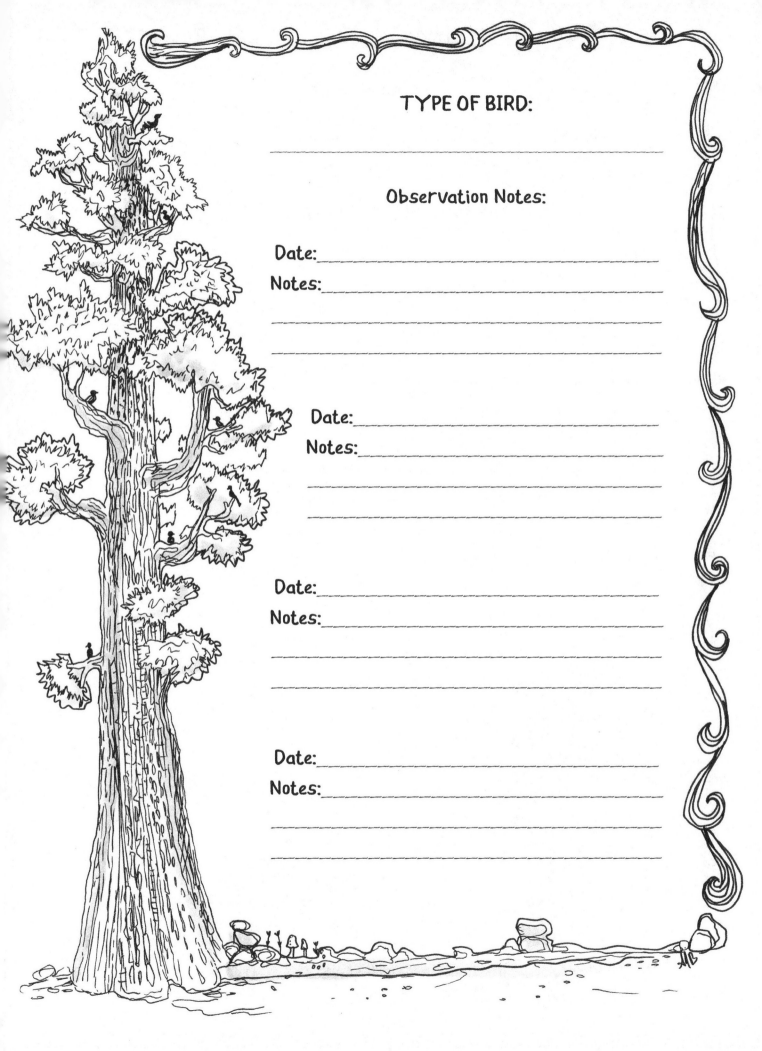

TYPE OF BIRD:

_____

Observation Notes:

Date:_____

Notes:_____

_____

_____

Date:_____

Notes:_____

_____

_____

Date:_____

Notes:_____

_____

_____

_____

Date:_____

Notes:_____

_____

_____

_____

TYPE OF BIRD:

Common Name: _____

Scientific Name: _____

Five Facts About This Type of Bird:

1._____

_____

2._____

_____

3._____

_____

4._____

_____

5._____

_____

_____

_____

_____

Draw or Photograph a Female:

Draw or Photograph a Male:

Just for Fun

1976
USA

Write, Doodle or Sketch!

Research Challenge!

Can You Identify and Color Each North American Bird?

1. _____

_____

2. _____

_____

3. _____

_____

4. _____

_____

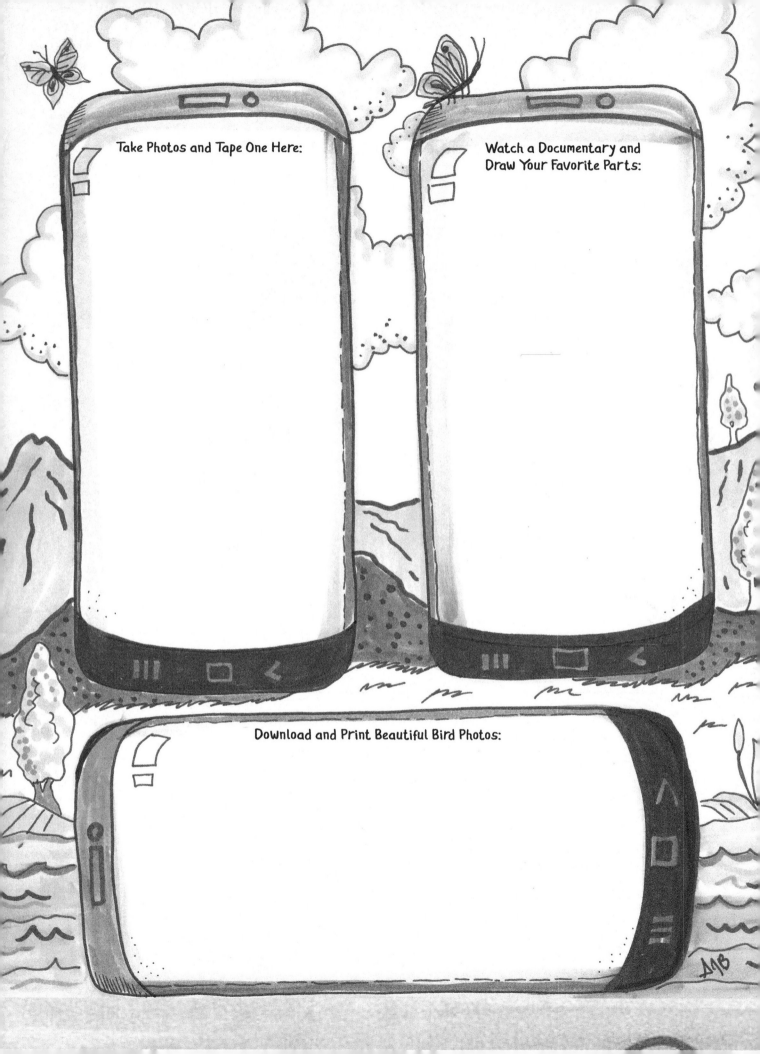

Take Photos and Tape One Here:

Watch a Documentary and Draw Your Favorite Parts:

Download and Print Beautiful Bird Photos:

Draw the Feet of Different Types of Birds in Your Region

Type of Bird:

1st Day Spotted:

My Nest

My Egg

Draw Me

My Feathers

Research

Notes_____
_____
_____
_____
_____
_____
_____
_____

My Habitat

My Food

My Enemies

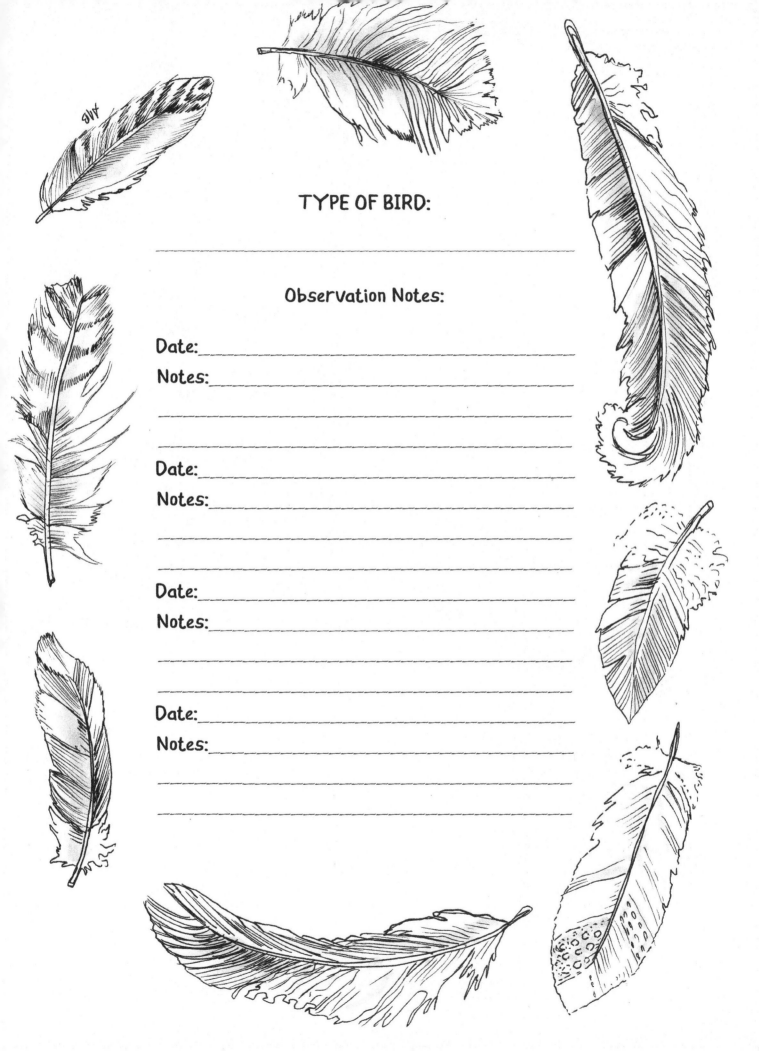

TYPE OF BIRD:

_____

Observation Notes:

Date:_____

Notes:_____

_____

_____

Date:_____

Notes:_____

_____

_____

Date:_____

Notes:_____

_____

_____

Date:_____

Notes:_____

_____

_____

Draw or Photograph a Female:

Draw or Photograph a Male:

TYPE OF BIRD:

Common Name: _____

Scientific Name: _____

Five Facts About This Type of Bird:

1._____
_____
_____

2._____
_____
_____

3._____
_____
_____

4._____
_____
_____

5._____
_____
_____
_____

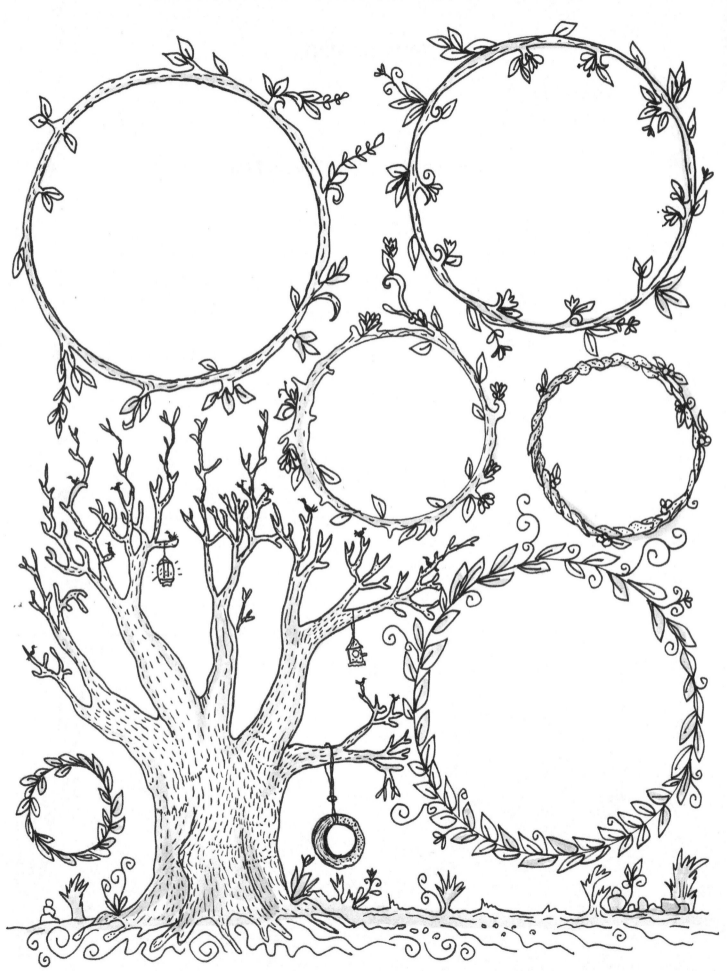

Read a Book about Birds and Take Notes:

_____
_____
_____
_____
_____
_____
_____
_____
_____
_____

Copy a picture from your book:

Nature Poem:
(Copy one or write your own)

_____

_____

_____

_____

_____

_____

_____

_____

_____

_____

_____

_____

_____

_____

_____

_____

Draw the Faces of Different Types of Birds in Your Region

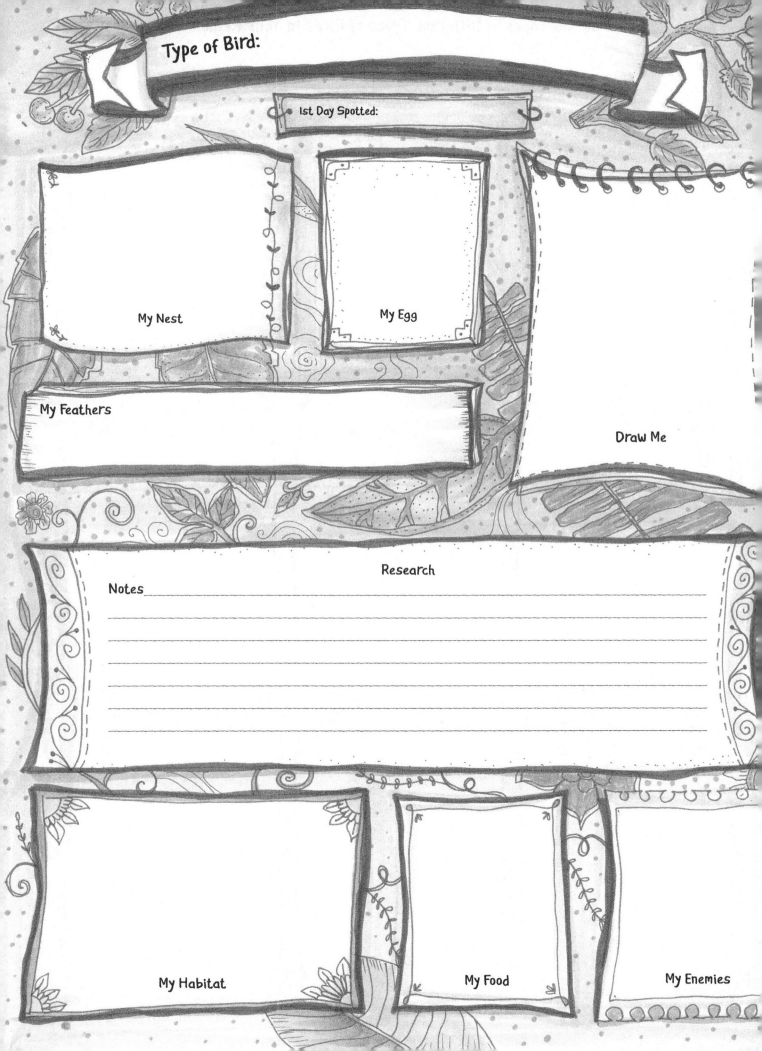

Type of Bird:

1st Day Spotted:

My Nest

My Egg

My Feathers

Draw Me

Research

Notes

My Habitat

My Food

My Enemies

TYPE OF BIRD:

_____

Observation Notes:

Date:_____

Notes:_____

_____

_____

Date:_____

Notes:_____

_____

_____

Date:_____

Notes:_____

_____

_____

Date:_____

Notes:_____

_____

_____

TYPE OF BIRD:

Common Name: _____

Scientific Name: _____

Five Facts About This Type of Bird:

1._____
_____

2._____
_____

3._____
_____

4._____
_____

5._____
_____
_____
_____

Draw or Photograph a Female:

Draw or Photograph a Male:

Take Photos and Tape One Here:

Watch a Documentary and Draw Your Favorite Parts:

Download and Print Beautiful Bird Photos:

Research Challenge!

Can You Identify and Color Each North American Bird?

1._____
_____
_____

2._____
_____
_____

3._____
_____
_____

4._____
_____

Add Birds to the Drawing

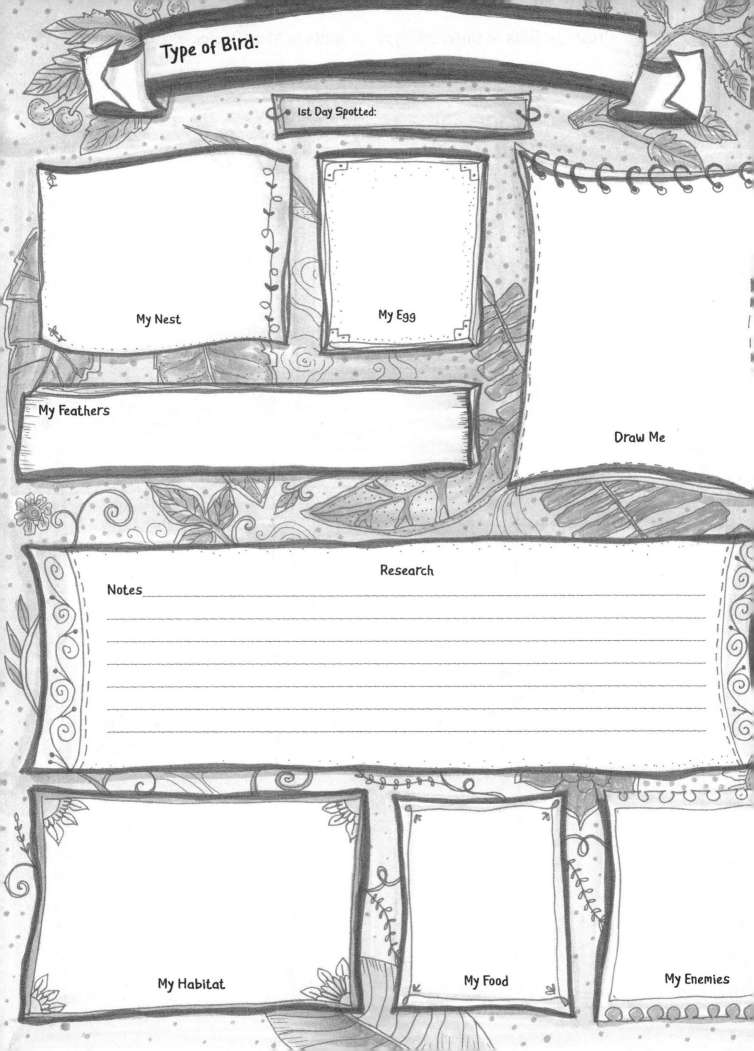

Type of Bird:

1st Day Spotted:

My Nest

My Egg

My Feathers

Draw Me

Research

Notes

My Habitat

My Food

My Enemies

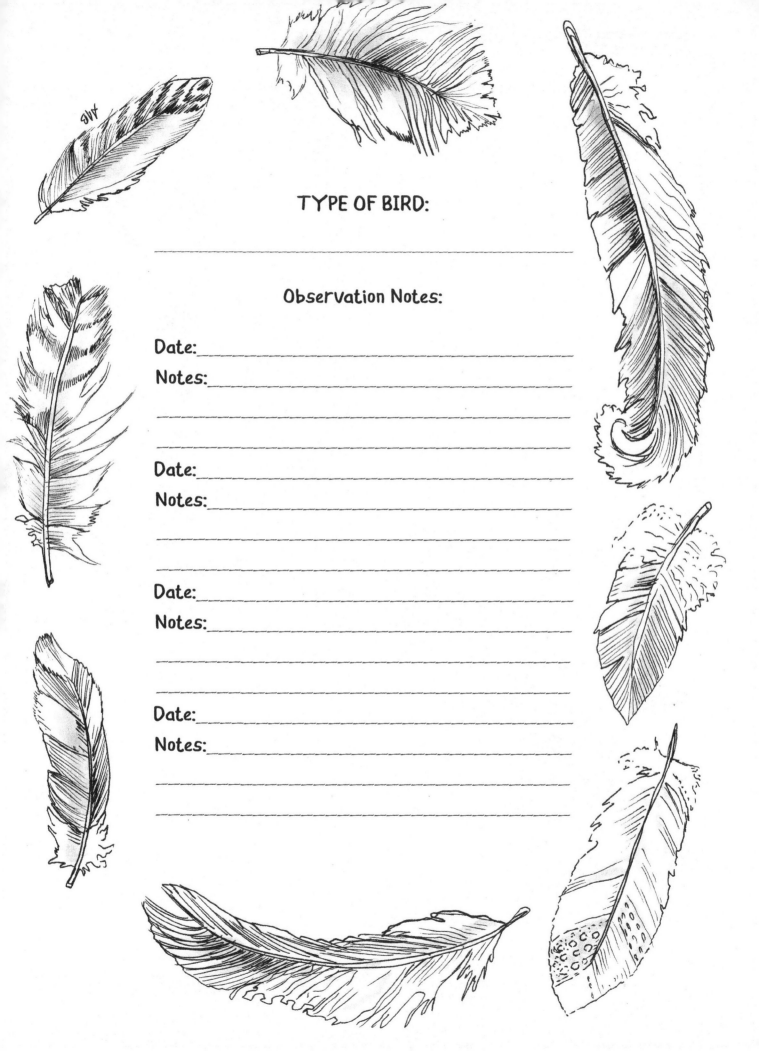

TYPE OF BIRD:

_____

Observation Notes:

Date:_____

Notes:_____

_____

_____

Date:_____

Notes:_____

_____

_____

Date:_____

Notes:_____

_____

_____

Date:_____

Notes:_____

_____

_____

Draw or Photograph a Female:

Draw or Photograph a Male:

TYPE OF BIRD:

Common Name: _____

Scientific Name: _____

Five Facts About This Type of Bird:

1._____
_____
_____

2._____
_____

3._____
_____
_____

4._____
_____

5._____
_____
_____
_____

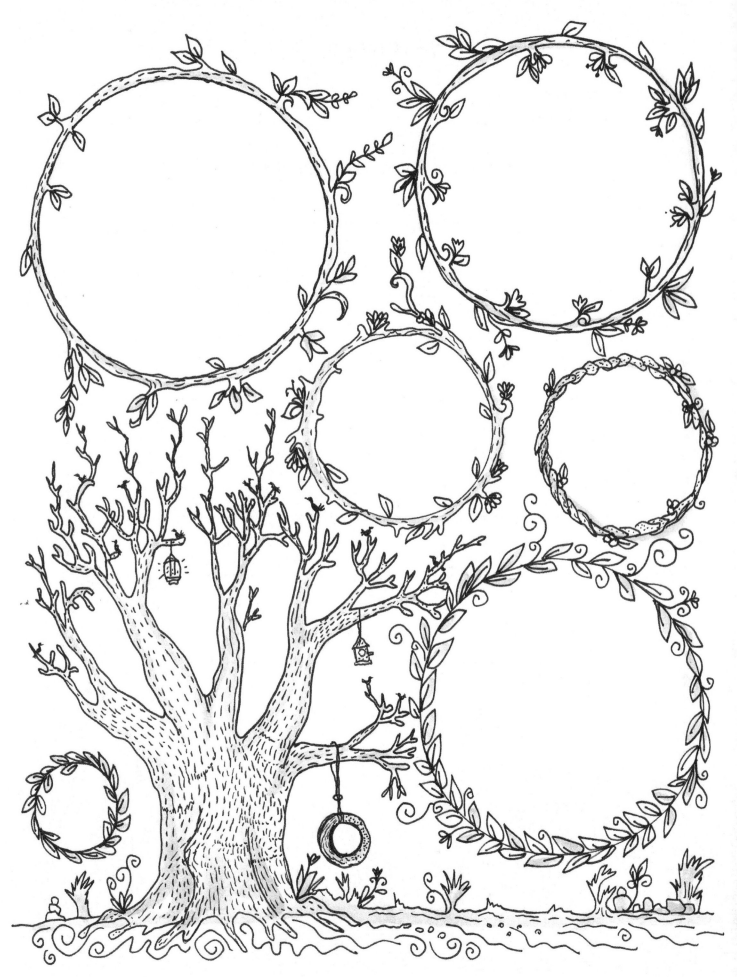

Read a Book about Birds and Take Notes:

_____

_____

_____

_____

_____

_____

_____

Copy a picture from your book:

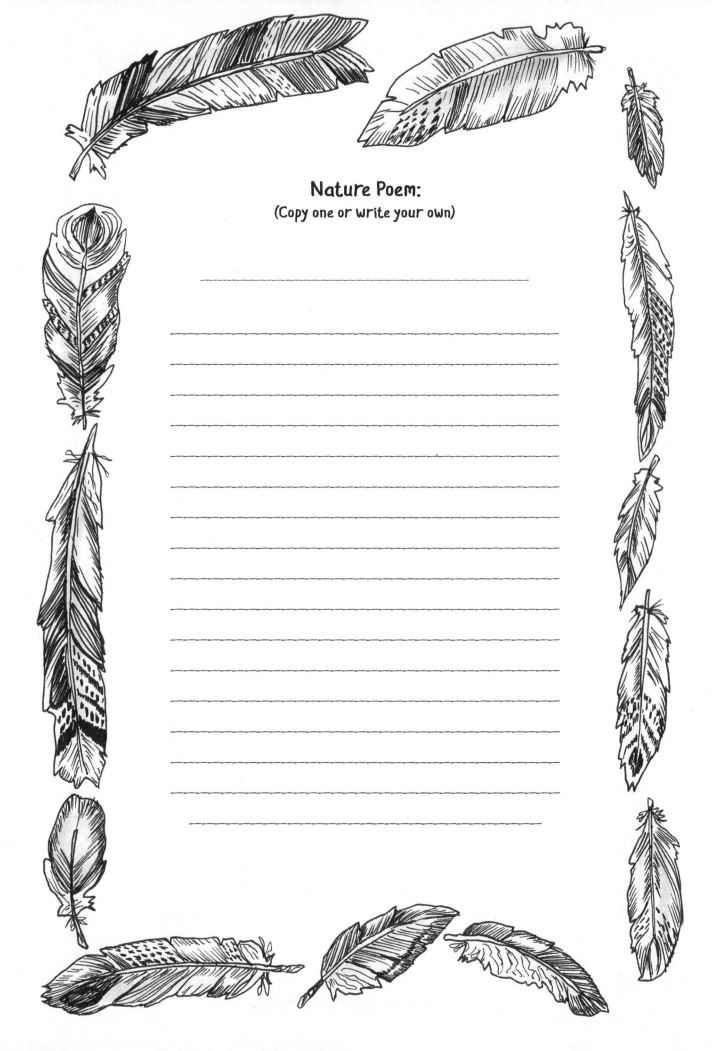

Nature Poem:
(Copy one or write your own)

Type of Bird:

1st Day Spotted:

My Nest

My Egg

My Feathers

Draw Me

Research

Notes _____
_____
_____
_____
_____
_____
_____
_____

My Habitat

My Food

My Enemies

TYPE OF BIRD:

_____

Observation Notes:

Date:_____

Notes:_____

_____

_____

Date:_____

Notes:_____

_____

_____

Date:_____

Notes:_____

_____

_____

Date:_____

Notes:_____

_____

_____

TYPE OF BIRD:

Common Name: _____

Scientific Name: _____

Five Facts About This Type of Bird:

1._____
_____

2._____
_____

3._____
_____

4._____
_____

5._____
_____
_____
_____

Draw or Photograph a Female:

Draw or Photograph a Male:

Just for Fun

1976
USA

Write, Doodle or Sketch!

Research Challenge!

Can You Identify and Color Each North American Bird?

1._____
_____
_____

2._____
_____
_____

3._____
_____
_____

4._____
_____

Add Birds to the Drawing

Type of Bird:

1st Day Spotted:

My Nest

My Egg

My Feathers

Draw Me

Research

Notes

My Habitat

My Food

My Enemies

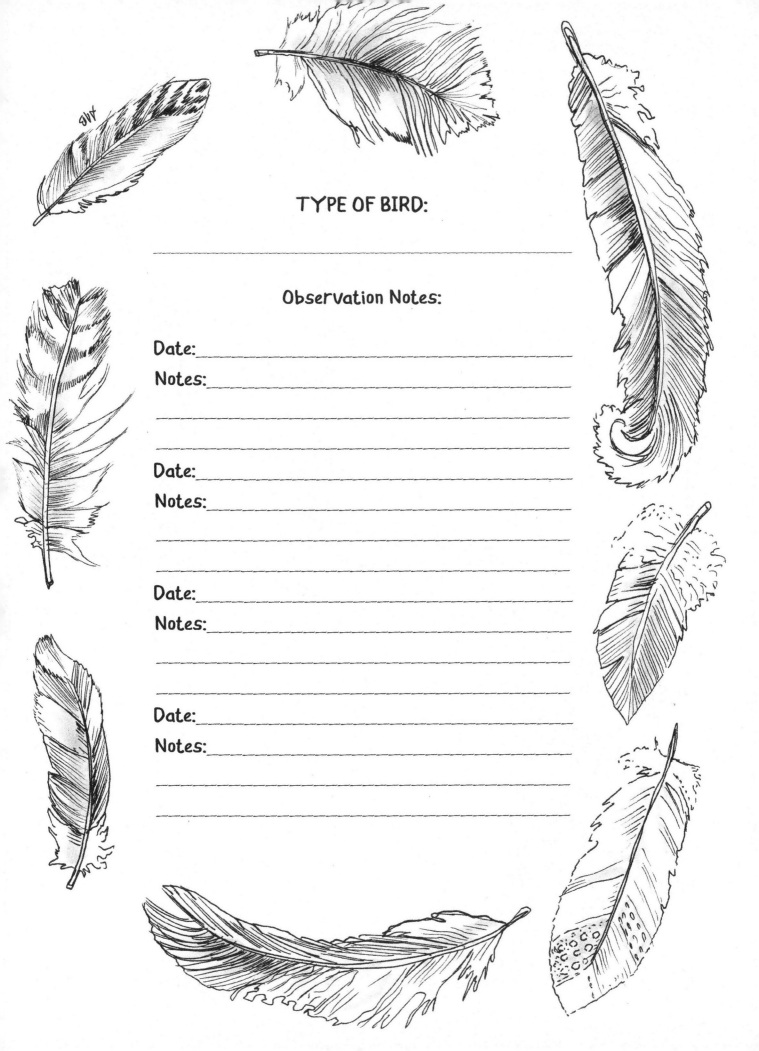

TYPE OF BIRD:

_____

Observation Notes:

Date:_____

Notes:_____

_____

_____

Date:_____

Notes:_____

_____

_____

Date:_____

Notes:_____

_____

_____

Date:_____

Notes:_____

_____

_____

Draw or Photograph a Female:

Draw or Photograph a Male:

TYPE OF BIRD:

Common Name: _____

Scientific Name: _____

Five Facts About This Type of Bird:

1._____
_____
_____

2._____
_____
_____

3._____
_____
_____

4._____
_____
_____

5._____
_____
_____
_____

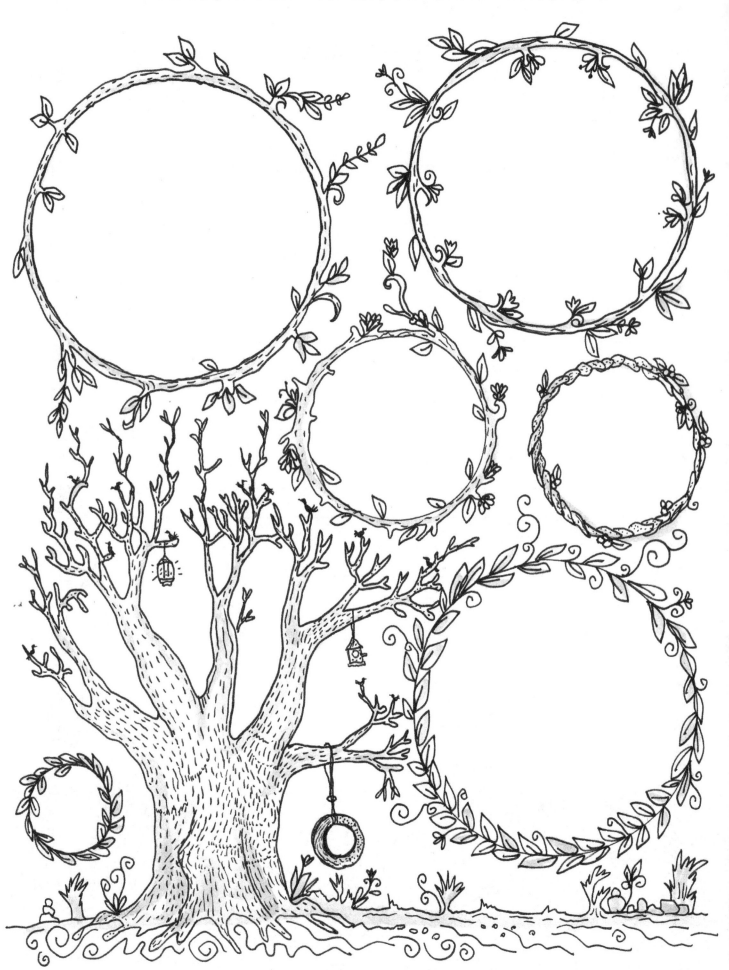

Read a Book about Birds and Take Notes:

Copy a picture from your book:

Nature Poem:
(Copy one or write your own)

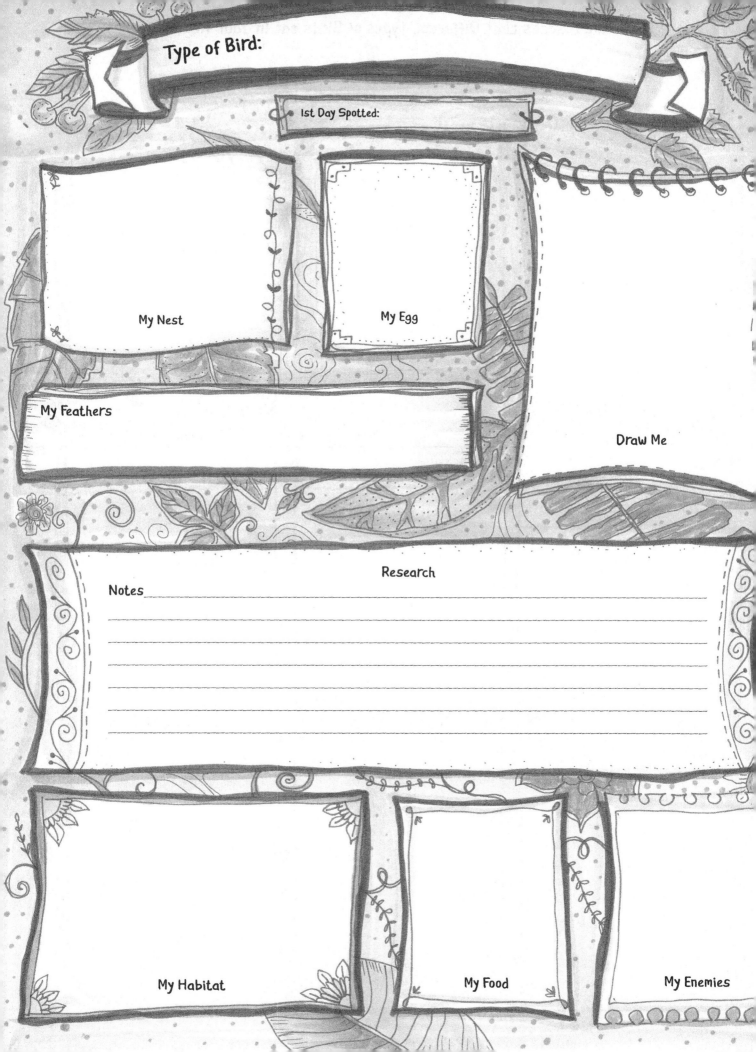

Type of Bird:

1st Day Spotted:

My Nest

My Egg

My Feathers

Draw Me

Research

Notes

My Habitat

My Food

My Enemies

TYPE OF BIRD:

_____

Observation Notes:

Date:_____

Notes:_____

_____

_____

Date:_____

Notes:_____

_____

_____

Date:_____

Notes:_____

_____

_____

Date:_____

Notes:_____

_____

_____

TYPE OF BIRD:

Common Name: _____

Scientific Name: _____

Five Facts About This Type of Bird:

1. _____
_____
2. _____
_____
3. _____
_____
4. _____
_____
5. _____
_____
_____
_____

Draw or Photograph a Female:

Draw or Photograph a Male:

Take Photos and Tape One Here:

Watch a Documentary and Draw Your Favorite Parts:

Download and Print Beautiful Bird Photos:

Research Challenge!

Can You Identify and Color Each North American Bird?

1._____

_____

_____

2._____

_____

_____

3._____

_____

_____

4._____

_____

_____

Add Birds to the Drawing

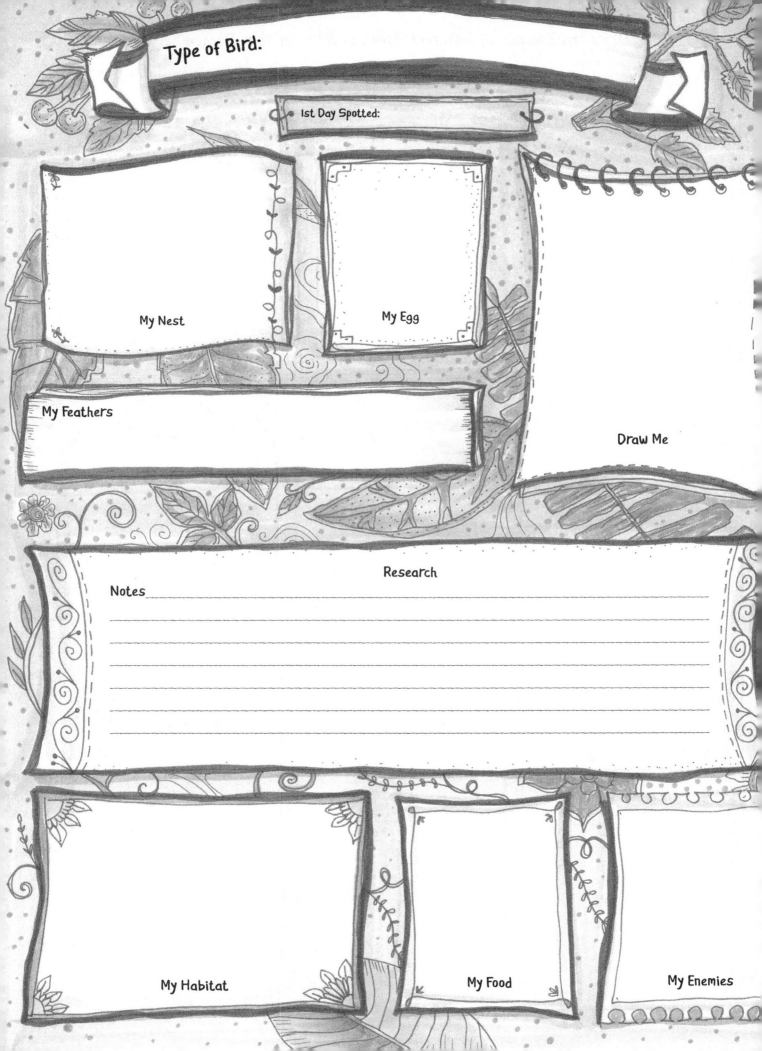

Type of Bird:

1st Day Spotted:

My Nest

My Egg

My Feathers

Draw Me

Research

Notes

My Habitat

My Food

My Enemies

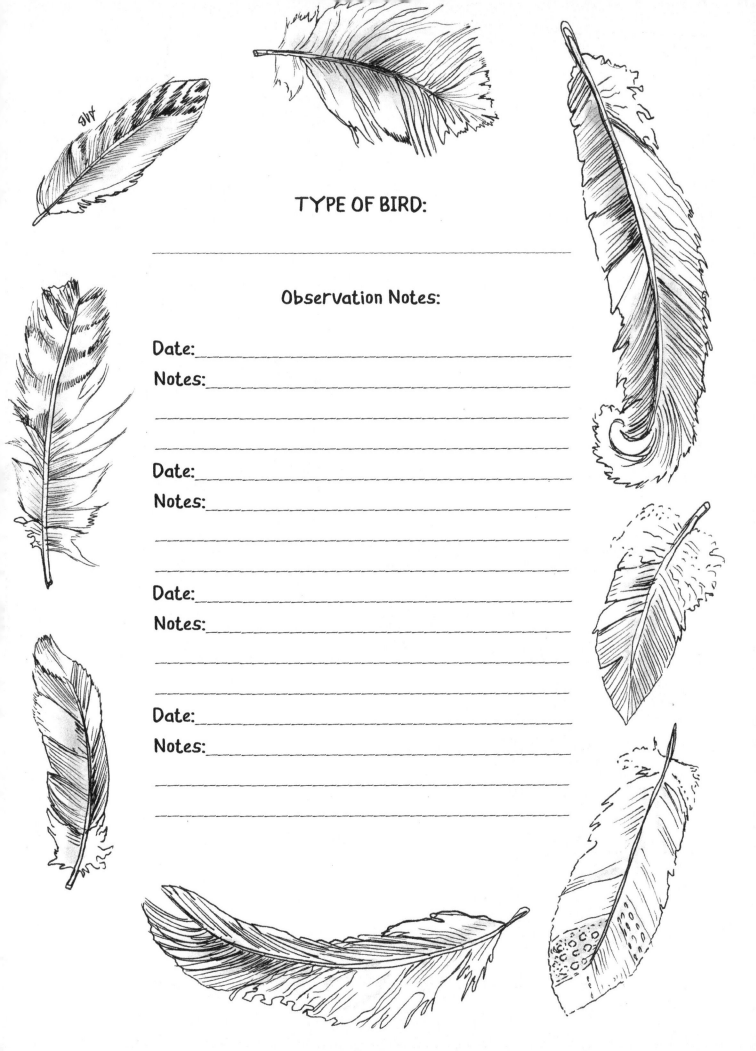

TYPE OF BIRD:

_____

Observation Notes:

Date:_____

Notes:_____

_____

_____

Date:_____

Notes:_____

_____

_____

Date:_____

Notes:_____

_____

_____

Date:_____

Notes:_____

_____

_____

Draw or Photograph a Female:

Draw or Photograph a Male:

TYPE OF BIRD:

Common Name: _____

Scientific Name: _____

Five Facts About This Type of Bird:

1._____
_____
_____

2._____
_____
_____

3._____
_____
_____

4._____
_____
_____

5._____
_____
_____
_____

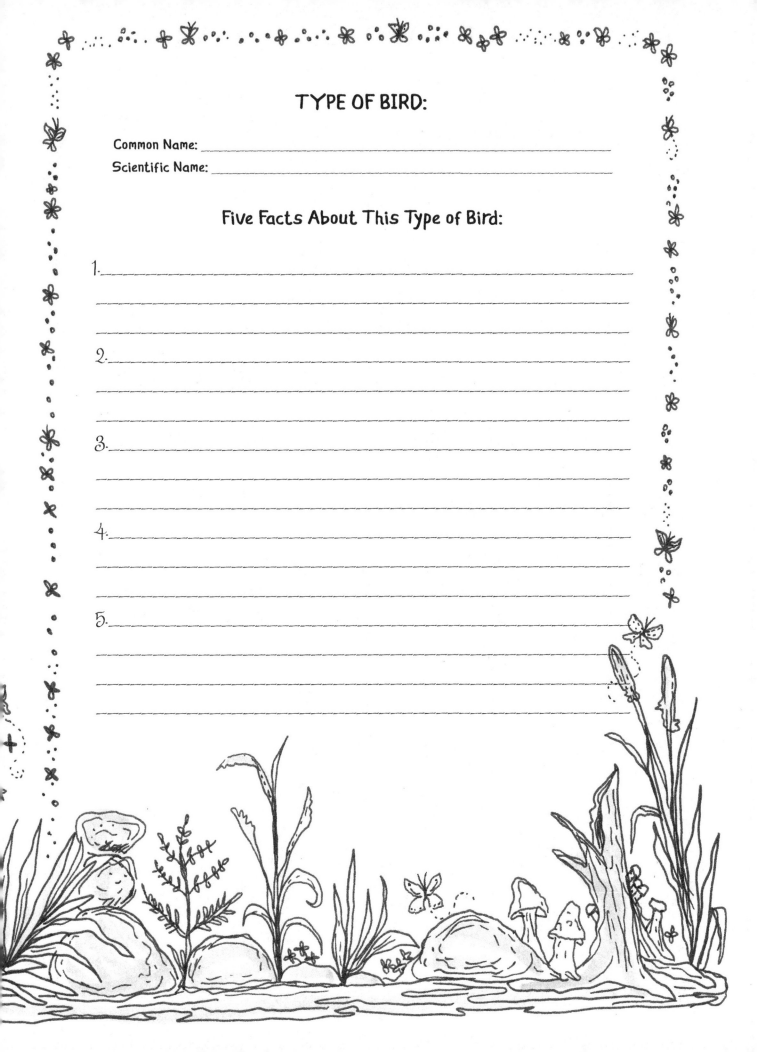

Just for Fun! Write, Doodle or Sketch!

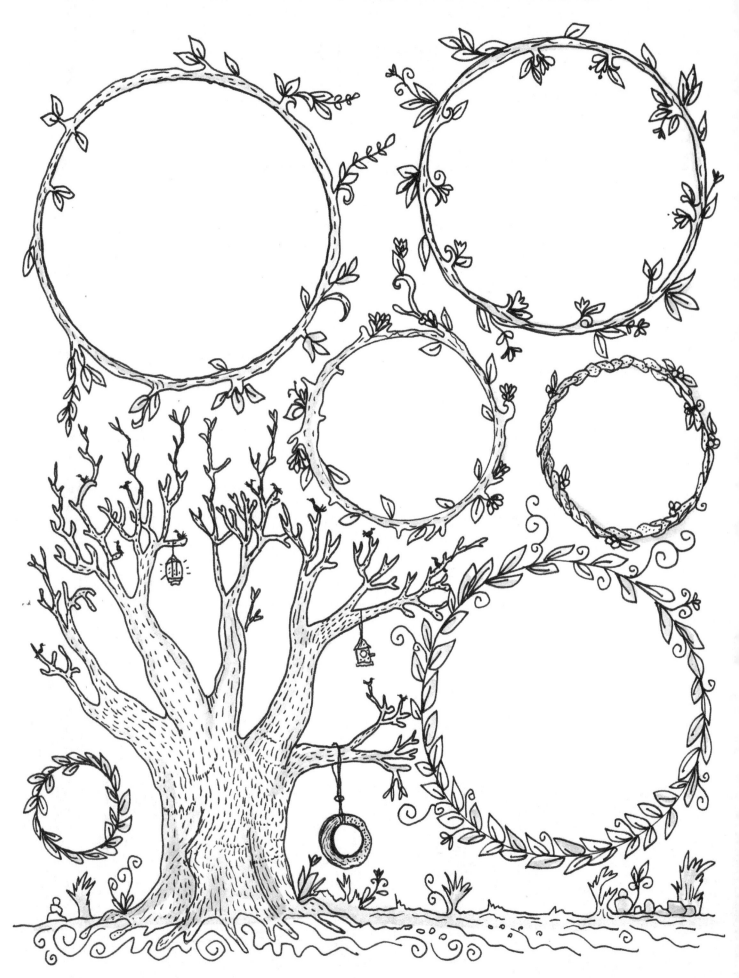

Read a Book about Birds and Take Notes:

_____

_____

_____

_____

_____

_____

_____

_____

Copy a picture from your book:

Add Birds to the Drawing

Just for Fun

1976
USA

Write, Doodle or Sketch!

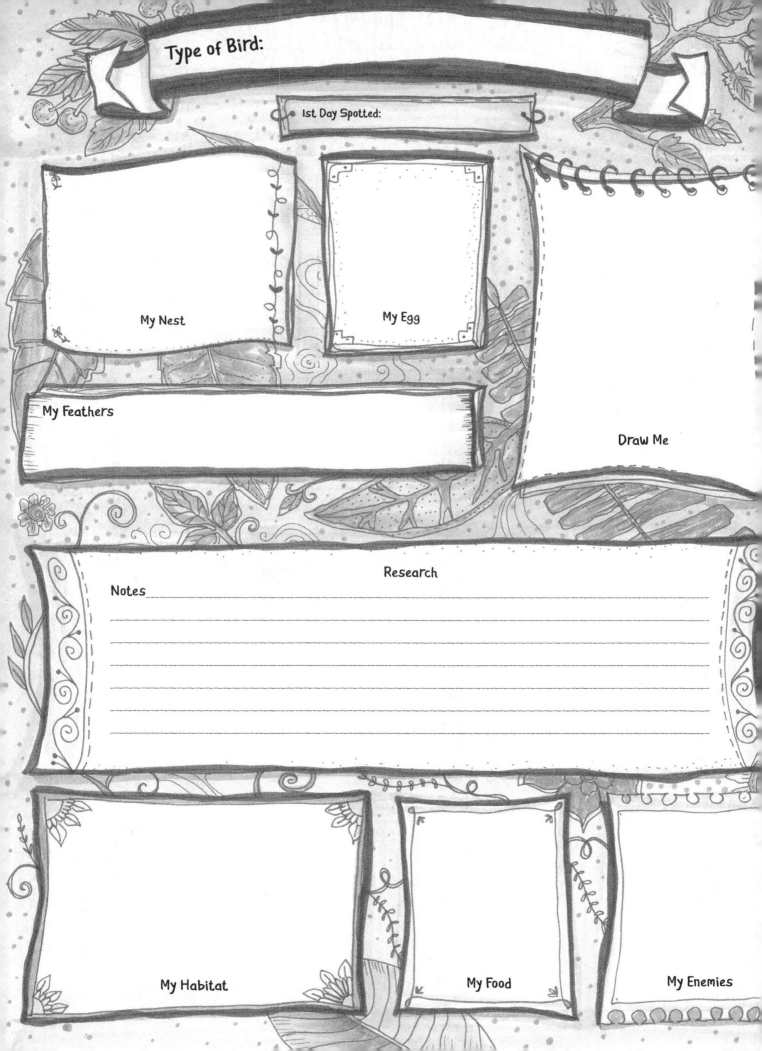

Type of Bird:

1st Day Spotted:

My Nest

My Egg

My Feathers

Draw Me

Research

Notes

My Habitat

My Food

My Enemies

TYPE OF BIRD:

_____

Observation Notes:

Date:_____

Notes:_____

_____

_____

Date:_____

Notes:_____

_____

_____

Date:_____

Notes:_____

_____

_____

Date:_____

Notes:_____

_____

_____

TYPE OF BIRD:

Common Name: _____

Scientific Name: _____

Five Facts About This Type of Bird:

1. _____
_____
2. _____
_____
3. _____
_____
4. _____
_____
5. _____
_____
_____
_____

Draw or Photograph a Female:

Draw or Photograph a Male:

Take Photos and Tape One Here:

Watch a Documentary and Draw Your Favorite Parts:

Download and Print Beautiful Bird Photos:

Nature Poem:
(Copy one or write your own)

Add Birds to the Drawing

Research Challenge!

Can You Identify and Color Each North American Bird?

1._____

_____

_____

2._____

_____

_____

3._____

_____

_____

4._____

_____

Type of Bird:

1st Day Spotted:

My Nest

My Egg

My Feathers

Draw Me

Research

Notes_____
_____
_____
_____
_____
_____
_____
_____

My Habitat

My Food

My Enemies

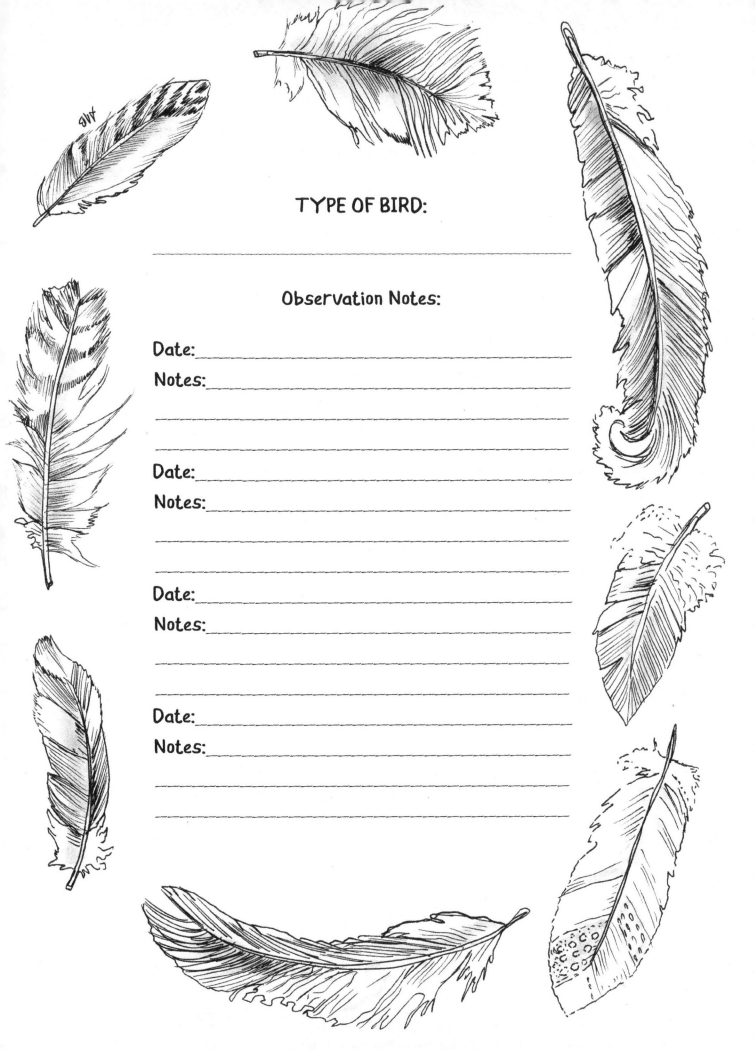

TYPE OF BIRD:

_____

Observation Notes:

Date:_____

Notes:_____

_____

_____

Date:_____

Notes:_____

_____

_____

Date:_____

Notes:_____

_____

_____

Date:_____

Notes:_____

_____

_____

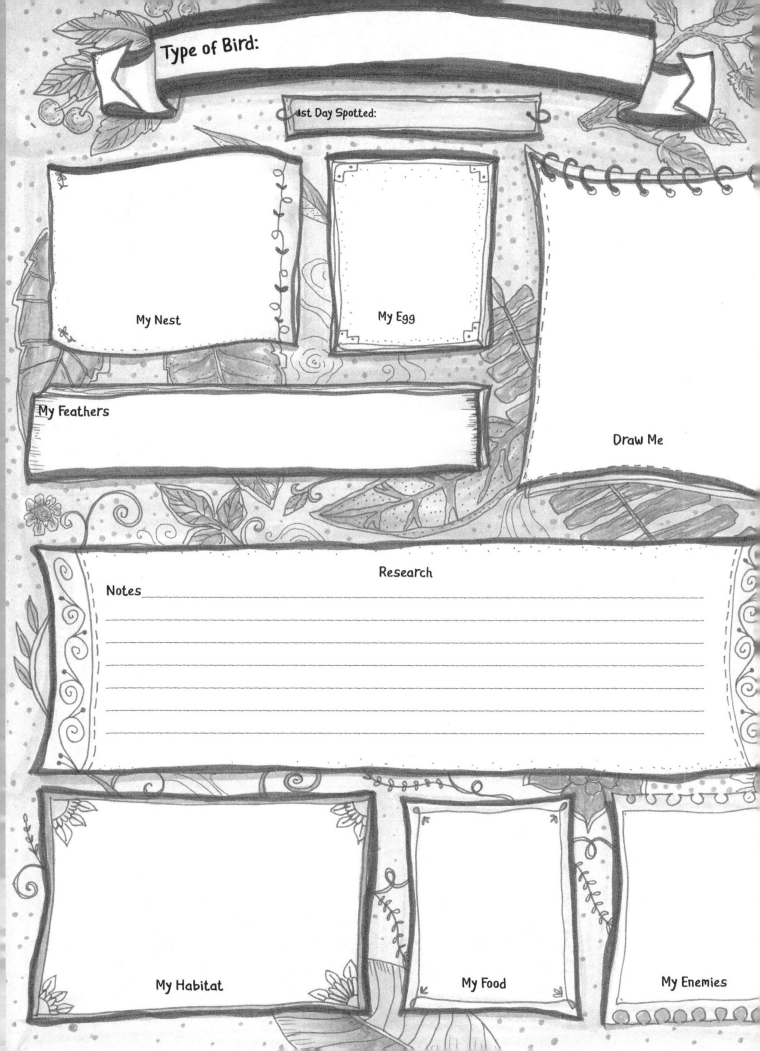

Type of Bird:

1st Day Spotted:

My Nest

My Egg

My Feathers

Draw Me

Research

Notes

My Habitat

My Food

My Enemies

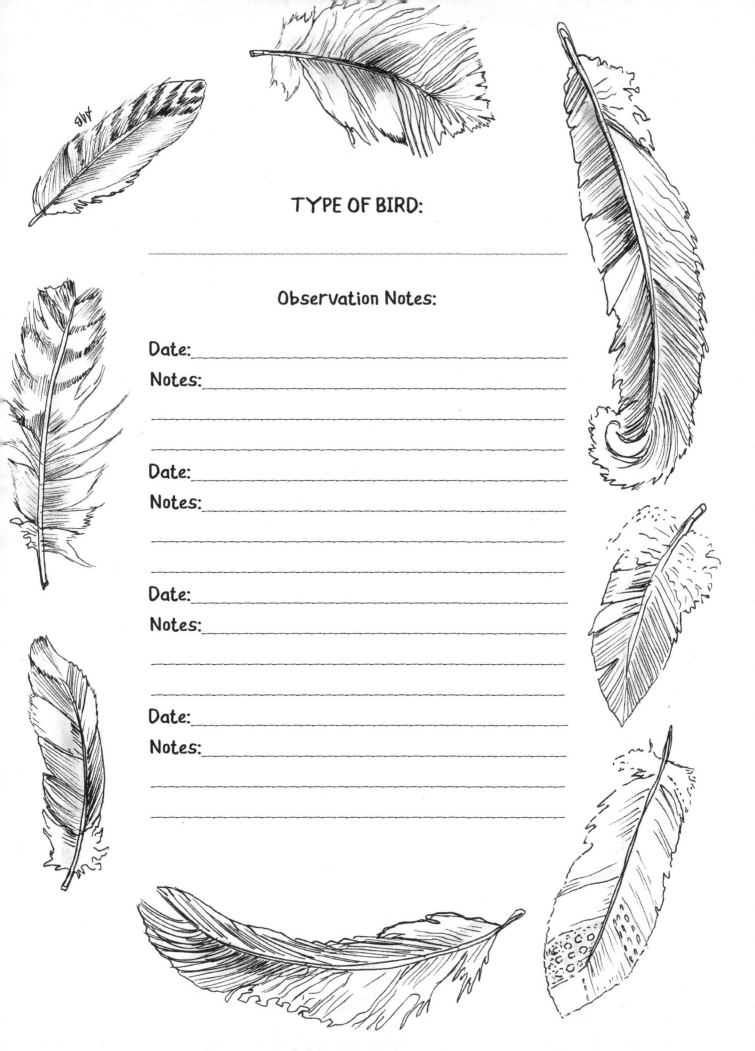

TYPE OF BIRD:

_____

Observation Notes:

Date:_____

Notes:_____

_____

_____

Date:_____

Notes:_____

_____

_____

Date:_____

Notes:_____

_____

_____

Date:_____

Notes:_____

_____

_____

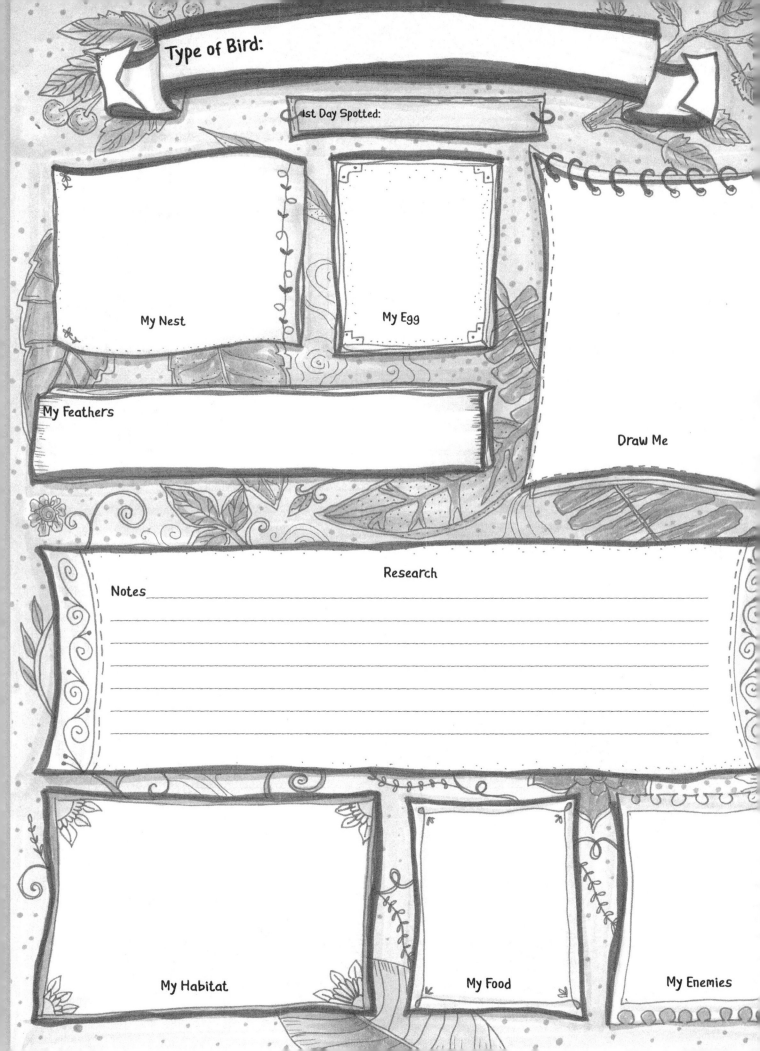

Type of Bird:

1st Day Spotted:

My Nest

My Egg

My Feathers

Draw Me

Research

Notes

My Habitat

My Food

My Enemies

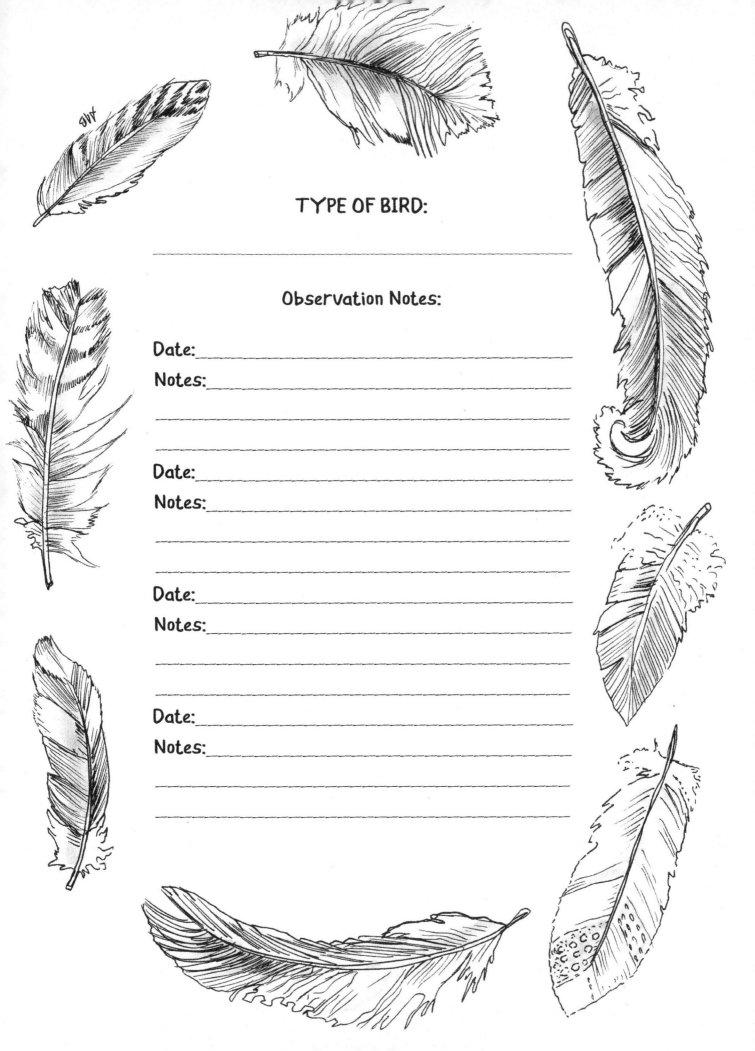

TYPE OF BIRD:

_____

Observation Notes:

Date:_____

Notes:_____

_____

_____

Date:_____

Notes:_____

_____

_____

Date:_____

Notes:_____

_____

_____

Date:_____

Notes:_____

_____

_____

Type of Bird:

1st Day Spotted:

My Nest

My Egg

My Feathers

Draw Me

Research

Notes

My Habitat

My Food

My Enemies

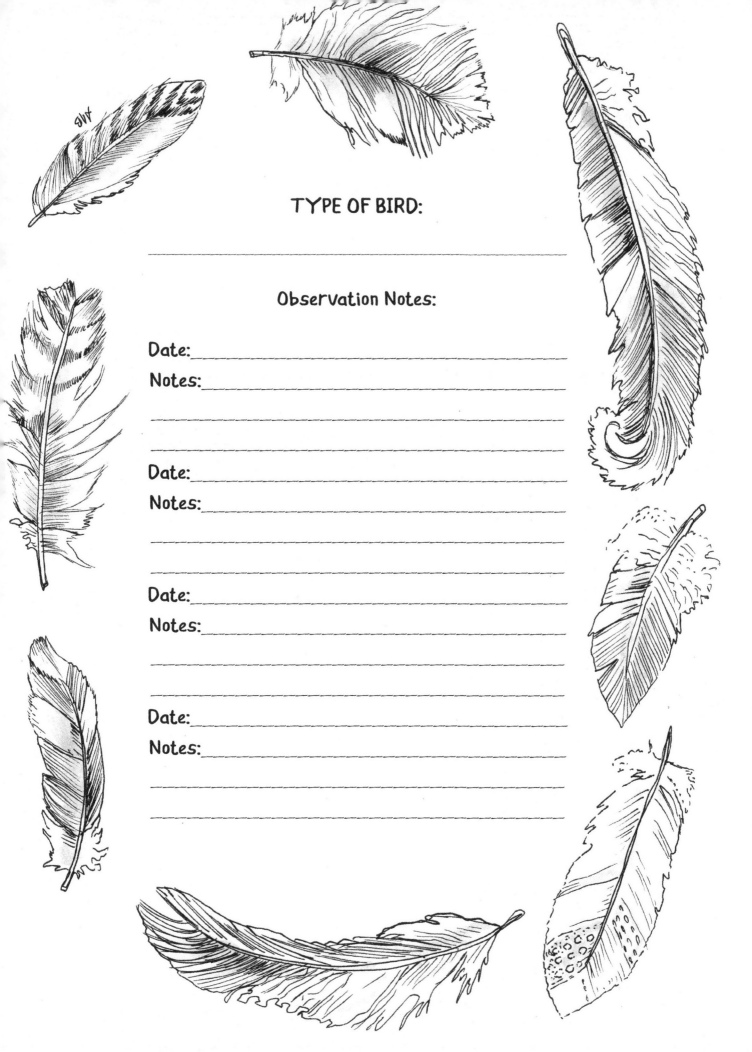

TYPE OF BIRD:

_____

Observation Notes:

Date:_____

Notes:_____

_____

_____

Date:_____

Notes:_____

_____

_____

Date:_____

Notes:_____

_____

_____

Date:_____

Notes:_____

_____

_____

Made in United States
Orlando, FL
22 March 2024